10-97

Thank You!

by
Liesl Vazquez

Illustrated by
Jenny Faw

 Peter Pauper Press, Inc.

WHITE PLAINS, NEW YORK

Copyright © 1995
Peter Pauper Press, Inc.
202 Mamaroneck Avenue
White Plains, NY 10601
ISBN 0-88088-789-3
Printed in China
7 6 5 4 3

Contents

Thank You

Dear Friend

For being part of my life.

For making ordinary days
special occasions.

For your laughter;
it is the greatest joy
of friendship.

I trust you with all
my secrets. Thank you
for never telling.

For always making time
to listen to me.

For helping me draw out
the different sides of
my personality.

For all the times
you've done the things
I wanted to do.
I owe you one . . . or two!

For leading me by example,
never by instruction.

I really appreciate
being able to talk to you
so freely and openly.

Your smiles always
warm my heart.

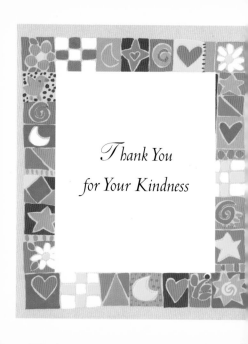

Thank You
for Your Kindness

I appreciate the little things
that you do for me
and for others.

In showing me that
sometimes it's just best to
let things happen.

In standing up for me
even though you may
disagree with my point
of view.

You have helped me believe
that true wealth is not
measured by possessions,
nor true beauty
by physical attributes.

In letting me cry
on your shoulder.

In being patient
and understanding.

I appreciate your encouraging
me to pursue my own path.

The tone of your voice
is always reassuring.

For always keeping a room for
me rent-free in your heart.

For lightening my load
during the darkest
of moments.

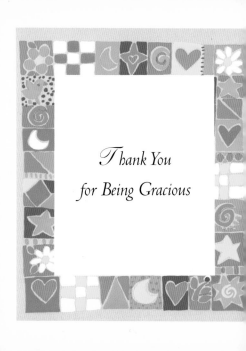

Thank You

for Being Gracious

You always
leave your door open.

You always
say the right thing.

You offer a helping hand,
and do the work.

Your smiles, your compassion,
and your generosity
enrich my life.

You cherish what is good
in others, and are tolerant
of what is less than good.

You share when you have much,
and never let on when
you have little.

You draw the circle of
your conversation so that
it always includes those
in your company.

You're quick to remember
other people's quiet
acts of kindness.

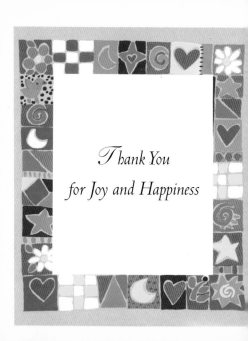

*T*hank You

for Joy and Happiness

For finding the joy
in being thankful.

For making this day
worth more than any other.

For believing that happiness
and wisdom are intertwined.

In extending yourself gladly.

In letting others be supportive
of you when you need it.

For your well-chosen words
that make a joyful noise.

For knowing that a wink
is as quick as a nod.

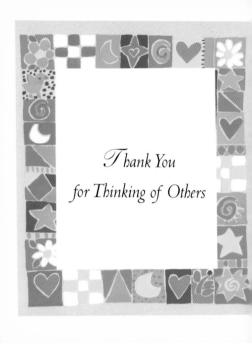

Thank You

for Thinking of Others

For thoughtful gestures,
never grand,
always sincere.

For knowing that a smile
is a small miracle.

Putting aside daily cares
to think of others
is time spent learning.

Thank you for nurturing
what others hold dear.

For anticipating what will
bring comfort to a
stranger, or a friend.

For understanding when
to stay, and when to go.

For knowing that a good day
becomes brighter when
caring is applied.

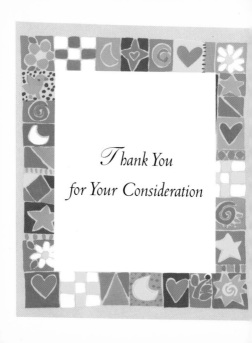

Thank You

for Your Consideration

Thank you for believing
that *please* carries at least
two meanings.

A friend may turn
the other cheek,
but never looks away.

For letting me mark
my own path to your door.

For helping me find peace
when I'm at war with myself.

Being secure in the knowledge
that tomorrow always comes,
but today is when help
is needed.

Good advice doesn't
spoil overnight.

A change of seasons doesn't
change a true heart.

For forgiving what I said,
because you know
what I mean.

Thank You

Dear Friend

For being part of
my self-discovery.

For thinking time shared
is worthwhile for
its own sake.

When I act silly, it's because
I'm comfortable enough
around you to do so.

I learn new things about myself
when we're together.

I'm honored that
you confide in me.

For being a pillar of strength,
but also knowing
when to bend.

For nurturing the seeds
of our relationship.

You're always there for me
when I need you.

For accepting me
as I am.

For growing with me
through laughter and love,
sorrow and joy.